Retroville Funnies

Based on the TV series *The Adventures of Jimmy Neutron, Boy Genius*
as seen on Nickelodeon®

ISBN 0-439-62347-2

12 11 10 9 8 7 6 5 4 3 2 1   4 5 6 7 8 9/0

Printed in the U.S.A.

First Scholastic printing, September 2004

Retroville Funnies

by David Lewman

SCHOLASTIC INC.

New York Toronto London Auckland Sydney
Mexico City New Delhi Hong Kong Buenos Aires

Boy Genius Blunders

What would Jimmy's name be if he were a ghost? Jimmy BOOtron.

What's Jimmy's favorite kind of tree?
Chemistry!

What did Jimmy get when he tried to invent a rocket-powered throwing stick?
A kaboomerang.

What's it called when Jimmy has to stay after school because of something he made?
Invention detention.

How is Jimmy Neutron like an air shaft?
He spends all his time inventing.

What did the germ say before it slid down Jimmy Neutron's throat?
"I'll be down in a Jimmy!"

6

What do you call Jimmy Neutron when he's deep in the rain forest?
A jungle Jim.

If Jimmy's friend Sheen was a car, what kind would he be?
A limosheen.

Is Jimmy Neutron noisy?
Yes, he's always making a rocket.

Who's short and knows all about purple fruit?
Jimmy Neutron, Boysenberry Genius.

Why did Jimmy crawl into a big glass jar?
He wanted to be a genius in a bottle.

9

Supersonic Silliness

Who brings colored eggs
and is made out of metal?
The Easter Robot.

What do mechanical frogs say?
Robot, robot.

What do you call a female
deer made out of metal?
A doebot.

What's really smart, follows orders, and melts in the spring?
A snowbot.

Why did the mad scientist destroy all the other scientists' workplaces?
He wanted to have the last lab.

Do neutrons ever laugh?
Only if they're particklish.

What's the best kind of dog for a scientist?
A laboratory retriever.

What did the atom say to the electron?
"Come on over—we're having a particle!"

Why didn't the physicist keep dating the biologist?
There was no chemistry between them.

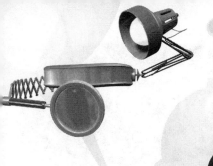

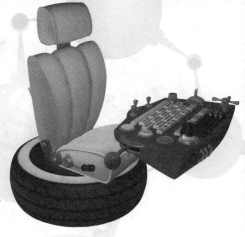

What do scientists eat for breakfast?
Eggs Spearmint.

What do cows invent?
Gizmoos.

Where can you buy the best brains?
Gray Mart.

15

Fetch This!

Who is Goddard's favorite hero?
Joan of Bark.

Why did Goddard have gear for breakfast?
It's a dog-eat-cog world.

What are Goddard's
favorite nuts?
Lug nuts.

Why did Jimmy reprogram Goddard
to bark higher?
He wanted to raise the woof.

Why isn't Goddard ever quoted in the paper?
He always speaks arf the record.

Does Goddard have a college degree?
Yes, he has his dogtorate.

Where would Goddard like to visit in outer space?
The planet Arf.

Why did Goddard burrow into the volcano? He wanted to be a hot diggety dog.

19

Why did Goddard fly to the North Pole?
He wanted to be a chilly dog.

What does Goddard like to put on his burger?
Mustard and gadget.

Why does Goddard eat so many microchips?
He's on a high-cyber diet.

Why did Jimmy give Goddard
a cake?
  It was his cyberthday.

Why did Goddard
sprout horns?
  He wanted to be
  a bulldog.

Know-it-all Knock-knocks

Carl: Knock, knock.
Jimmy: Who's there?
Carl: Alpaca.
Jimmy: Alpaca who?
Carl: I'll pack a lunch and we'll have a picnic.

Sheen: Knock, knock.
Jimmy: *Who's there?*
Sheen: Carlos.
Jimmy: *Carlos who?*
Sheen: Carl owes me five bucks—where is he?

25

Prepare For Ultra-laughs!

What do Sheen's friends turn into when he talks about his collection? *Ultra Bored.*

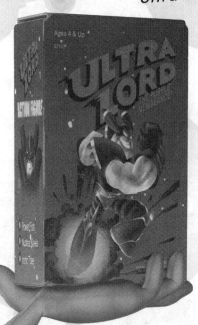

What's the best way to describe Jimmy and his hair?
Short and to the point.

Bad Hair Busts!

How did Jimmy's hair get that way? I think it got caught in a swirlwin

Do you like my hairstyle?
Looks more like a hair pile.

What do they call
Jimmy's mom at the
barber shop?
Mother-of-Swirl.

29

Carl Crack-ups

Why does Carl spend so much time at the zoo? Because he's a real llama's boy.

What's Carl's favorite vegetable? Llama beans.

What did Carl do
with the picture of
his favorite animal?
He had it llamanated.

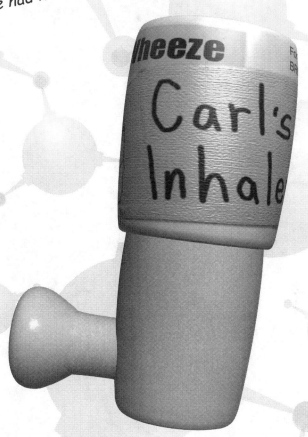

heeze

Carl's
Inhale

What do you call Carl
with lettuce on his head?
A Wheezer salad.

Why didn't your dad shove his decoy out of the way?
He didn't want to push his duck.

What do you call a duck in a carton?
A quack-in-the-box.

What do you get when you cross a duck and a snake?
A diamondquack rattler.

How do Ms. Fowl and her boyfriend dance?
Beak to beak.

Why did Ms. Fowl set her alarm for 5:00 a.m.?
She wanted to be the early bird.

34

How did Ms. Fowl learn to speak at such an early age? *Beginner's cluck.*

Why do Ms. Fowl and Jimmy get along? *They're both eggheads.*

Why did the electron leave home?
He ran away to join the circuit.

Why didn't the birdcatcher put Ms. Fowl in a cage?
She squawked him out of it.

Where did Nick Dean
go before grade
school?
Nursery cool.

What do you call a horse who's a genius? A big neigh-it-all.

38

What do you call a rat who's a genius?
A big gnaw-it-all.

TOP SECRET

What do you call a pig who's a genius?
Albert Swinestein.

Fundamental Funnies

What's Jimmy's favorite band?
In Think.

Why is it hard to sleep when Jimmy spends the night?
Because he's really bright.

Why did Jimmy bring cattle into his lab?
He wanted to do an oxperiment.

What kind of trousers does Jimmy wear?
Smartypants.

What do you get when you cross Jimmy with a turtle? *Something very inshelligent.*

Why did you call Jimmy "edgy"?
Because he's really sharp.

43

If Jimmy were Peter Pan, where would he live?
Clever Land.

44

Why did you think Jimmy would win the race?
Because in class he's really quick.

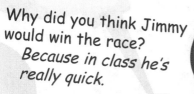

How did everybody find out Jimmy has a big head?
He couldn't keep it under his hat.

What's the difference between Chicago and the Vortex girl? One's the Windy City and the other's the Witty Cindy.

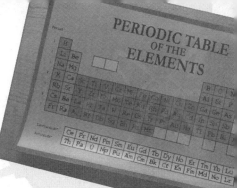

What's every scientist's favorite movie?
"101 Equations."

What kind of exercise equipment would Jimmy never be?
A dumbbell.

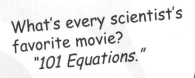

Why does Jimmy like flying in his rocket?
He always has a blast.